nickelodeon

# PUPTA[illegible]C ACT[illegible]S

Parragon

Bath • New York • Cologne • Melbourne • Delhi
Hong Kong • Shenzhen • Singapore

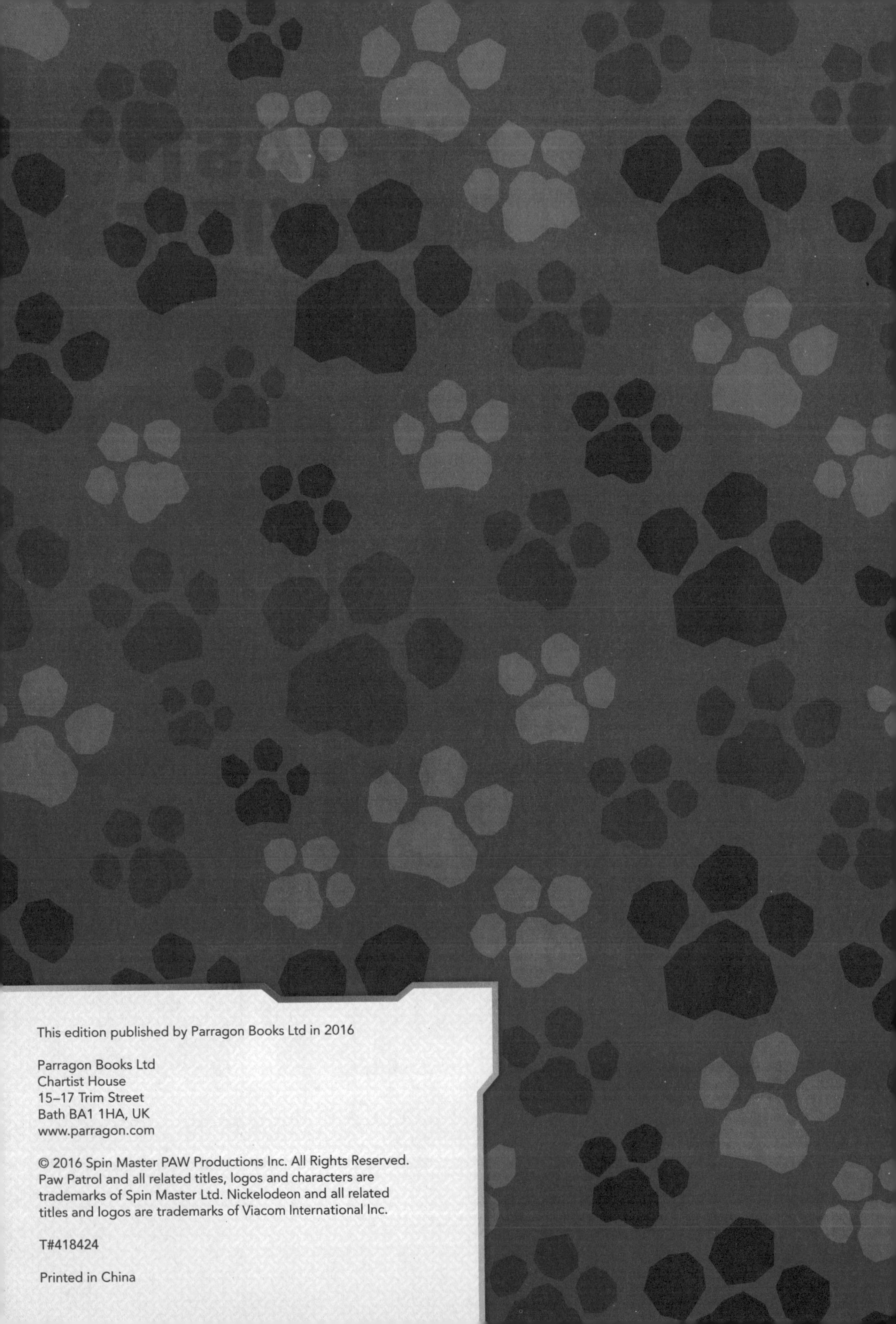

This edition published by Parragon Books Ltd in 2016

Parragon Books Ltd
Chartist House
15–17 Trim Street
Bath BA1 1HA, UK
www.parragon.com



T#418424

Printed in China

# YELP FOR HELP!

When someone's in trouble, it's all paws on deck!
Draw a line to match each member of the PAW Patrol to their name.

A RUBBLE

B SKYE

C MARSHALL

D CHASE

E ROCKY

F ZUMA

Answers on page 31

# HEROIC HOUNDS

Each member of the PAW Patrol has their own symbol that shows their special skill. Tick the correct symbol next to each pup.

## 1 RUBBLE

A ☐ B ☐ C ☐

## 2 SKYE

A ☐ B ☐ C ☐

## 3 ZUMA

A ☐ B ☐ C ☐

## 4 CHASE

A ☐ B ☐ C ☐



Answers on page 31

# HIS NOSE KNOWS

Chase's amazing nose can follow the scent of just about anything. That's what makes him a great police pup! Help him find Ryder by following his nose through the maze.

Answers on page 31

# SPOT THE DIFFERENCE

Marshall's spots make him really easy to spot! Look carefully at these two pictures and see if you can spot five differences. Colour in one of Marshall's flames for each difference you find.

Answers on page 31

# WHO WOULD YOU SEND?

One of Ryder's jobs as the leader of the PAW Patrol is to choose which pup is right for each job. Who would you send for each of these rescues? Tick the right box.

**1.** A kitten is stranded out at sea. You'll need a boat to reach her!

Would you send:

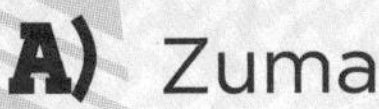

☐

**B)** Rocky

☐

**2.** Rocks are blocking some train tracks.
You'll need a digger to clear them!

Would you send:

☐

**B)** Rubble

☐

**3.** There's a fire in Adventure Bay. You'll need a hose to put it out!

Would you send:

☐

**B)** Chase

☐

Answers on page 31

# RUBBLE ON THE DOUBLE!

Rubble loves to get his paws dirty helping others. Join the dots to finish the picture of him and his bucket scoop, then colour it all in using your brightest pencils or crayons.

# READY TO ROLL!

Ryder and the PAW Patrol are always ready! Draw lines to connect each missing piece to the correct place in the picture. Colour in one paw for each one you get right.

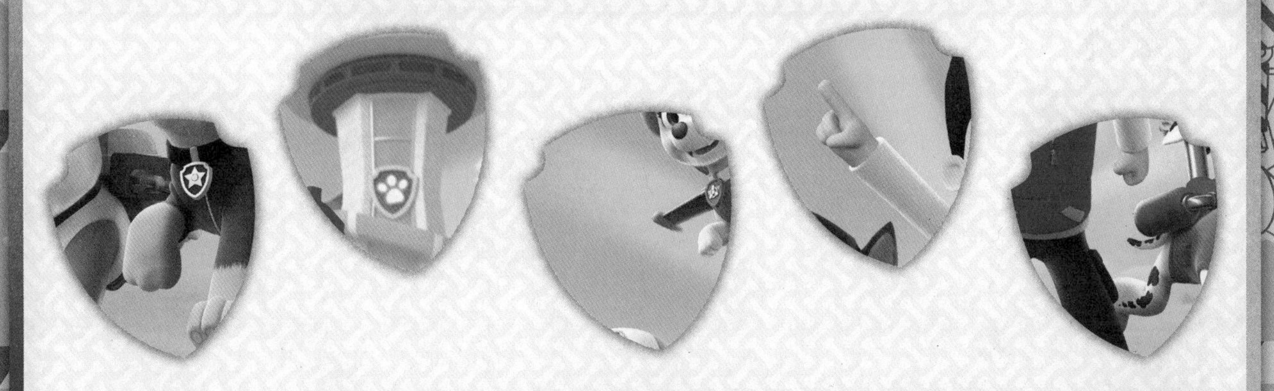

Answers on page 31

# ALL FIRED UP

Answers on page 31

# WHAT IS RUBBLE BUILDING?

Rubble is building something for the PAW Patrol. Can you see what it is?
Place a tick next to the correct answer.

- ☐ KENNEL
- ☐ CAR
- ☐ LIGHTHOUSE
- ☐ BOAT

Answers on page 31

# YELP FOR HELP!

Colour in the whole PAW Patrol team before they race into action!

# SHADOW PLAY

Chase has been using his torch to make shadows of the other PAW Patrol pups! Draw lines to match his friends to their correct shadows.

Answers on page 31

# GREEN MEANS GO

Rocky is PAW Patrol's problem solver! Use all your brain power to finish this picture by matching the numbers to the colour code.

## COLOUR CODE

**1** = dark green **2** = light green **3** = grey

**4** = light grey **5** = blue **6** = pink

# PAIR OF PUPS

Rubble knows that good friends always share, so he's sharing his bone with Zuma! Which two pictures of the pup heroes are the same? Draw a circle around them.

Answers on page 31

# ON THE MOVE

When the PAW Patrol rush to the rescue, their Pup Houses turn into rescue vehicles! Draw a line to match each pup to their vehicle.

Answers on page 31

# LET'S DIVE IN!

As PAW Patrol's water-rescue dog, Zuma is never afraid to make a splash! Trace over the lines below to copy the pup picture into the big grid. Then use the picture above as a guide to colour him in.

# WHICH PUP'S UP?

It's time for an exciting rescue in Adventure Bay! But Ryder's screen has mixed the letters up. Unscramble the letters to see which pup has been chosen to take part. Then draw that pup in the empty shield.

SARLHLAM

_ _ _ _ _ _ _ _



Answers on page 32

# PUP, PUP AND AWAY!

Skye's a pup who has just gotta fly! Join the dots to complete both of her wings, then colour her in.

# RUFF AND READY

Rocky and Marshall both have loads of energy and they love to play together! Circle the picture of them that is the odd one out.

Answers on page 32

# TIME FOR A PAW-TRAIT!

Ryder's taking pictures of all the members of the PAW Patrol! How many pups can you count in this picture? Write the number in the paw print below!

There are ___ pups in Ryder's photo.

Which member of PAW Patrol is missing?

Write their name here: _ _ _ _ _

Answers on page 32

# EXTREME CLOSE-UP!

Cap'n Turbot has been playing around with his telescope!
Draw lines between each member of the PAW Patrol and their close-up.

Answers on page 32

# UNDERWATER PUP!

Zuma is ready for anything!
Colour him in your favourite watery colours.

# THE RIGHT TOOLS

Rocky is ready to fix anything! Join the green dots to see one of the tools he always carries with him, then trace the letters underneath to write the answer.

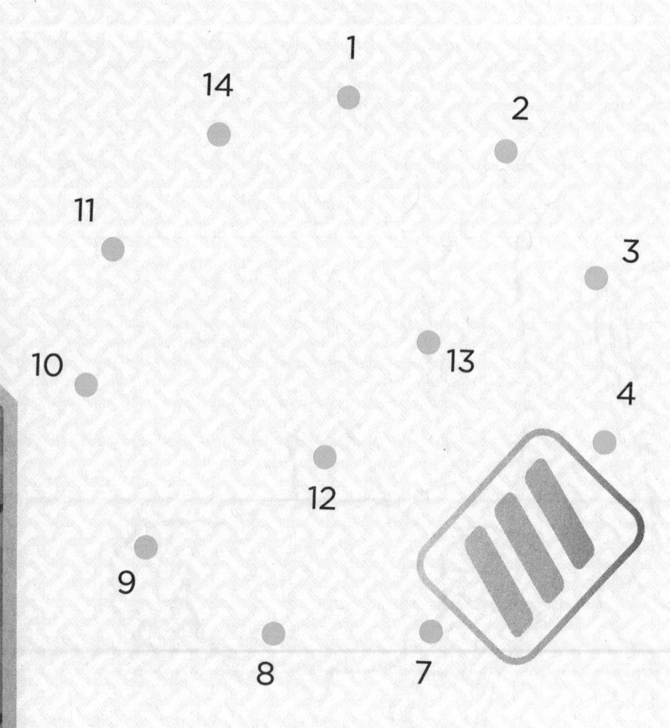


5

6

S P A N N E R



Answers on page 32

# WORD PLAY

Which of these words do you think describes PAW Patrol the best?
Draw a paw next to them!

BRAVE

SLOW

HEROES

STRONG

UNKIND

PLAY

TEAM

CATS

ADVENTURE

# COME IN, PAW PATROL!

Ryder started PAW Patrol when he adopted all the pups. Colour him in using your boldest colours.

When he needs to call the pups, Ryder uses the alarm on his PupPad. Colour in his PupPad, too.

# HAT'S OFF!

Rubble has left his hat behind! Help him through the maze to find it.

Answers on page 32

# HELPING OTHERS

PAW Patrol's mission is to help others when they need it. In the space below, draw a picture or write about a time when you helped someone.

# TEAM TIME!

The pups are teaming up in pairs for their next mission. Follow the lines to see who is paired up with who!

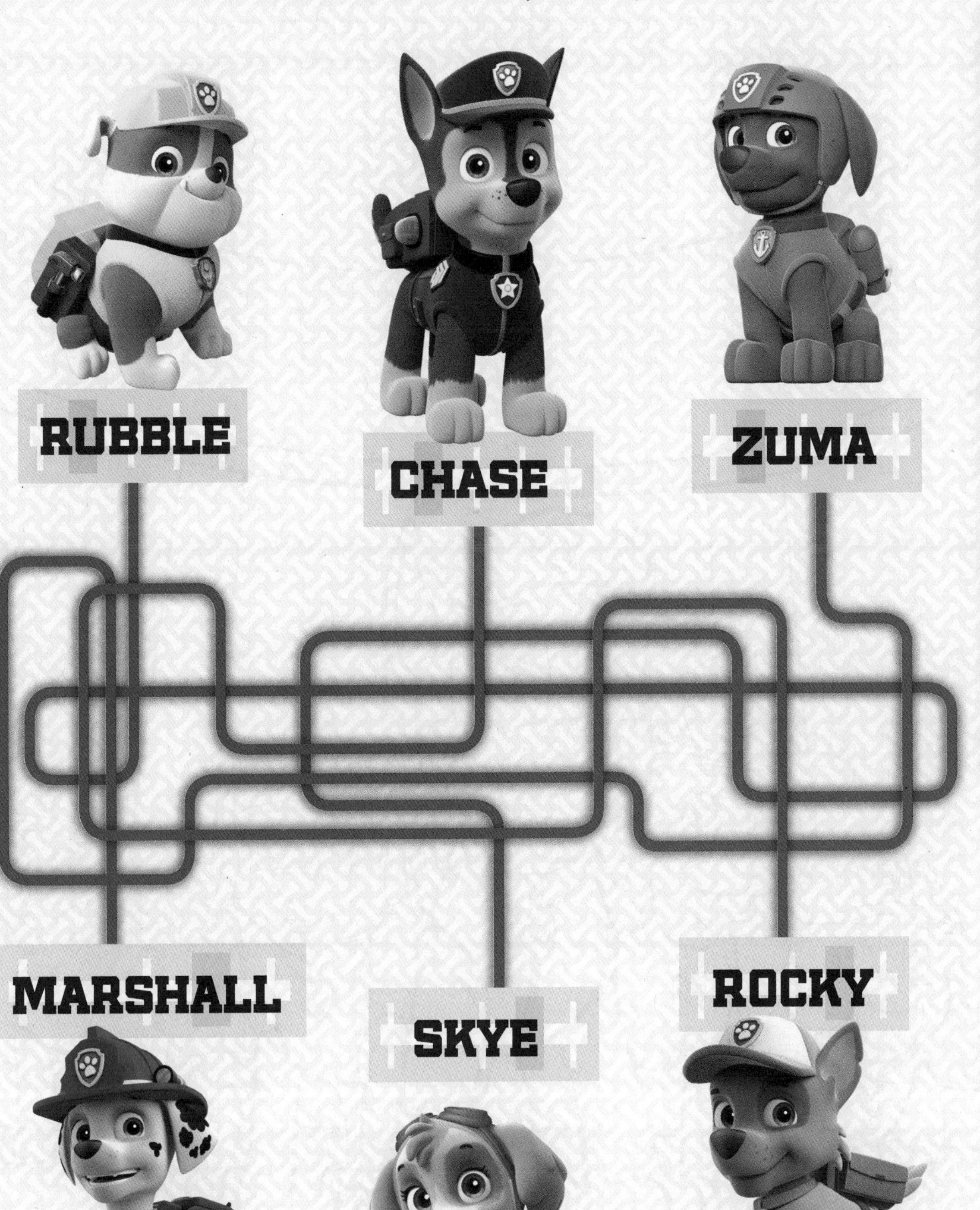


Answers on page 32

# MISSION COMPLETE!

Ryder, Chase, Marshall, Skye, Zuma, Rubble and Rocky are always ready to roll! Colour them in using your brightest colours. And don't forget, whenever there's trouble, just yelp for help!

# ANSWERS

**PAGE 3**
1-C, 2-F, 3-A, 4-D, 5-E, 6-B

**PAGE 4**
1-C, 2-B, 3-B, 4-A

**PAGE 5**

**PAGE 6**

**PAGE 7**
1-A, 2-B, 3-A

**PAGE 9**

**PAGE 10**
Path B

**PAGE 11**
Rubble is building a lighthouse

**PAGE 13**
1-D, 2-C, 3-B, 4-A

**PAGE 15**

**PAGE 16**

# ANSWERS

**PAGE 18**
Marshall

**PAGE 20**
Picture 3 is the odd one out

**PAGE 21**
There are 5 pups in Ryder's photo
Chase is missing from the photo

**PAGE 22**

**PAGE 24**
Spanner

**PAGE 27**

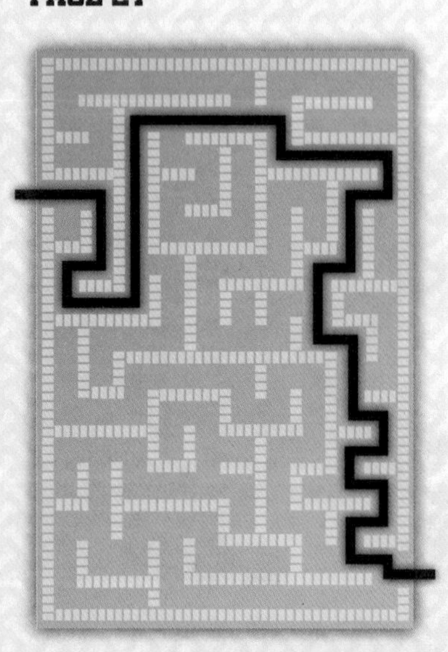

**PAGE 29**